THE BEEZER BOOK 1997

This book belongs to...

James Ashley Merry.
211. Bromsgrove Road
Redditch. wicked cool
With love and Best Wishes
from Gran and Grandad.
Christmas 1996.

Printed and Published in Great Britain by D. C. Thomson and Co., Ltd.,
185 Fleet Street, London EC4A 2HS.
© D. C. Thomson and Co., Ltd., 1996. ISBN 0-85116-619-9.
E.A.N. 9-780851-166193.

It's a pleasure doing business with you, sir.

BATH SHOWROOM

Har. Money down the drain.

That bloke's Jack Oozy. He's in the bath business and he's cleaning up.

CITY DUMP

Time I was down in the dumps.

And —

Perfectamundo!

Soon —

GEEZER'S BARGAIN BATHS

Watch me soft soap this customer.

DAFT DINOSAURS —
— and why they became extinct.

Fattysaurus lived on giant apples. It ate so much that it burst!

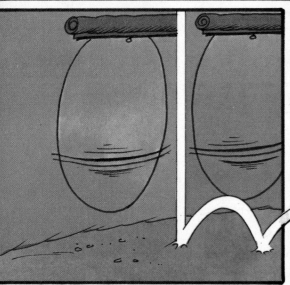

BABY CROCKETT

Me's in a school Christmas play today.

Don't laugh when me gets changed.

Me's playing a little people inna play.

Me'll go and get me's pal, Tommy.

All my helpers are ill, Baby. Can you help?

Wow! It's the real Santa Claus!

Whee! Santa thinks me's one of his elves!

DAFT DINOSAURS —

— and why they became extinct.

Blinkosaurus could run at 40 km per hour. Sadly, it couldn't see as far as its nose!

Today we're going back in time to study the year 1997!

That's great, Teacher!

A class from the future is on a field trip —

Put on your suits of invisibility!

No-one from the past must be allowed to see us!

Meanwhile —

If I'm so Brainy why am I carrying all the food?

PICNIC

The BEEZER GANG have THE TIME OF THEIR LIVES!

A FULL LENGTH FEATURE STORY

After the picnic —

What is it? Can we sell it?

The saucer's huge! Can't wait to see the cup!

I think we've found a time machine!

Look what we've just found!

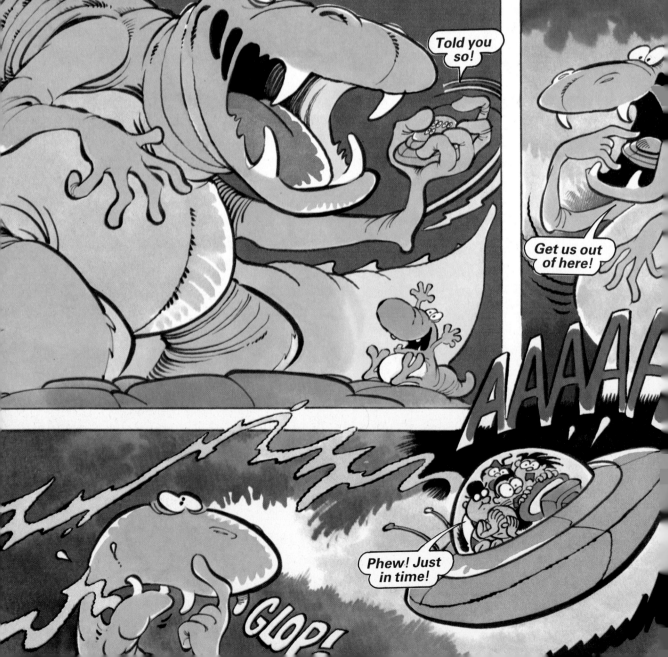

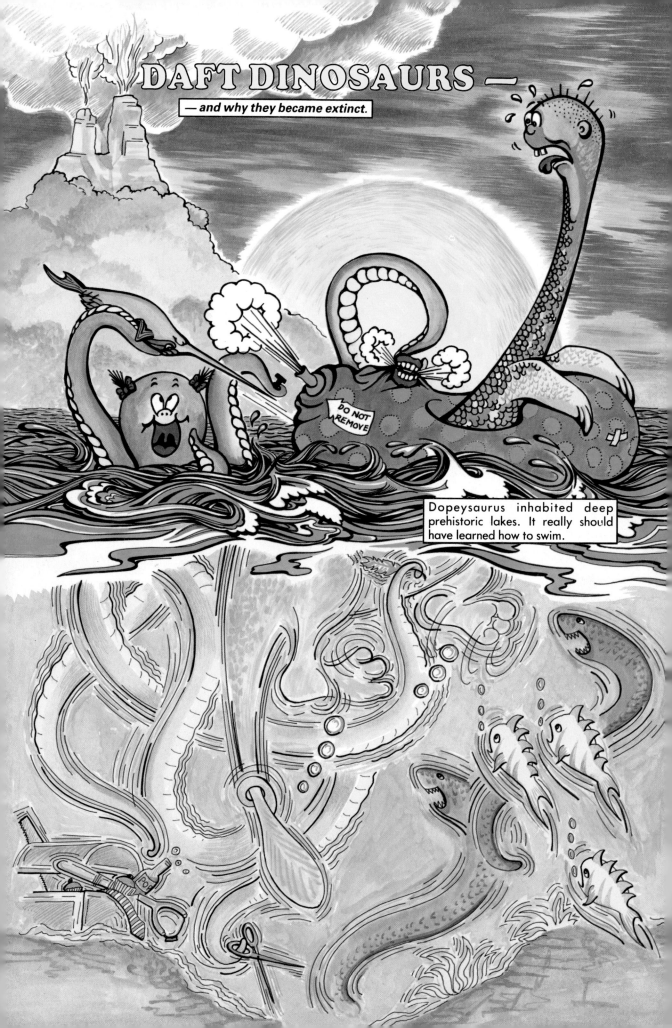

DAFT DINOSAURS —
— and why they became extinct.

Dopeysaurus inhabited deep prehistoric lakes. It really should have learned how to swim.

THE Banana Bunch

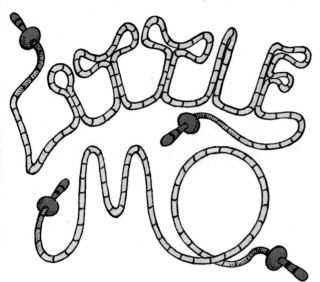

One, two . . .

Har! Har! Mo's enjoying her skipping!

Let me help you, Mo!

There! Now you've got two ropes!

Try this rope!

DAFT DINOSAURS —

— and why they became extinct.

MUGSY'S LAIR

Mosaurus picked fights with the Mugsysaur, which was four times taller than it.

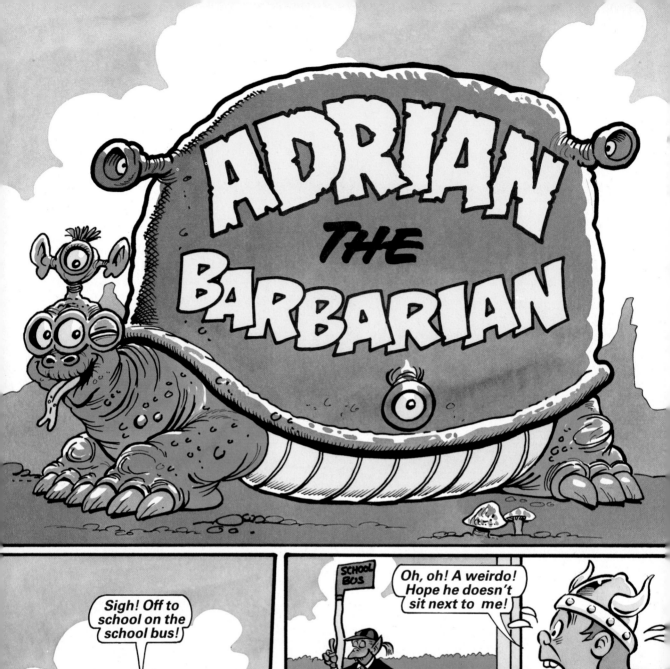

ADRIAN THE BARBARIAN

Sigh! Off to school on the school bus!

Oh, oh! A weirdo! Hope he doesn't sit next to me!

Hi!

Argh!

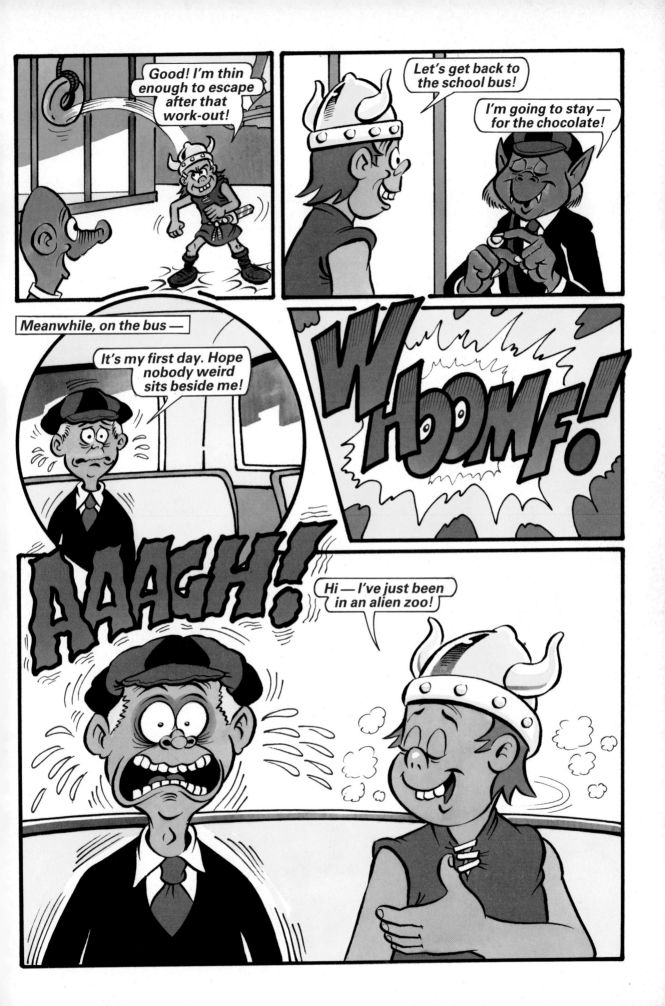

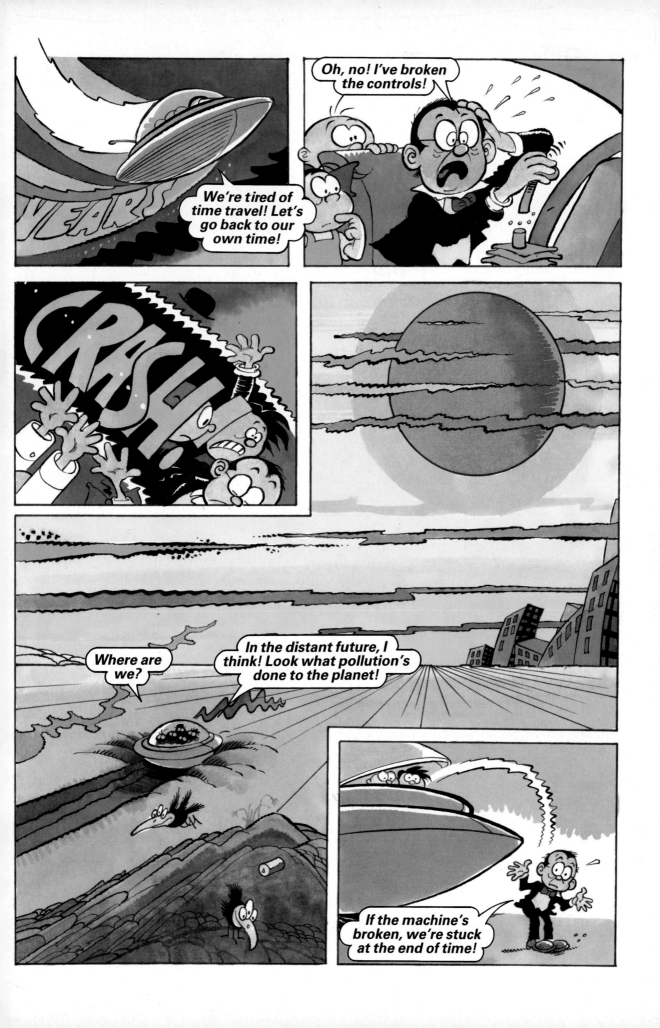

THE NUMSKULLS

That was a great ghost story. Wonder what I can do now?

I'll make a suggestion!

VISIT THE HAUNTED HOUSE!

And so —

Funny! I've had a sudden urge to come here! It's scary, though!

HAUNTED HOUSE

Back home —

DAFT DINOSAURS

— and why they became extinct.

The early Crockettiles loved sweet things. Pity they didn't know it was bad for their teeth.